MINING SITES IN CORNWALL

MINING SITES IN CORNWALL

(VOLUME 2)

by

Barry Atkinson

NOV. 1995

DYLLANSOW
TRURAN

First published 1994 by Dyllansow Truran, 'Trewolsta', Trewirgie, Redruth, Kernow.

© 1994 Barry Atkinson

ISBN No. 1 85022 052 2

Printed and bound by R. Booth (Bookbinder) Ltd (a subsidiary of Troutbeck Press), Antron Hill, Mabe, Penryn, Cornwall. Telephone: (0362) 373226.

IV

Abbreviations

Name of Mine - alternative title in brackets

D.   Chief periods of operation

L.   Location with Grid Reference number - 2½" Ordnance Survey

M/O. Mineral Output

S.   A description of the site as it appears today

Note: Many of the mines included in this volume are situated well off the beaten track and are often dangerously obscured from view by ferns, brambles and trees. A great deal of caution is therefore required of the individual when exploring these workings, especially as many old shafts and excavations are still open to the elements and only protected by a fence or crumbling stonework. Adits, or drainage tunnels, should not be entered unless one is with a person familiar with such workings. These narrow passageways, most of which are over a century old, are usually in a state of collapse and water-logged. It is also worth noting that permission should be sought from either the local farmer or landowner to view these mines as a large number now lie on private land.

Contents

Introduction

In my first publication 'Mining Sites in Cornwall and South West Devon' I described and categorised over 250 abandoned mines in the region, most of which had substantial remains to be seen at surface and were, for the most part, easily accessible. Scattered throughout the length and breadth of Cornwall, however, are the sites of many more mining ventures that deserve as much investigation although their names may not be so familiar to the newcomer in the field of industrial archaeology. Many of these lesser known mines were worked on a very small scale, often far away from the more prosperous mining areas, and sometimes consisted of a single shaft or adit worked by a few of the 'old men'. Others existed in close proximity to such renowned names as Dolcoath, United Mines, East Wheal Rose and South Caradon, but did not quite achieve the fame or success that these mines did, and are therefore not generally well documented. In many cases, mineral output from these workings was minimal or even non-existent, the sett being little more than an exploratory trial on a remote cliff face or far off river valley.

Over the past twenty years or so, widespread re-development in the county, including the ploughing up of old mining ground and road reconstruction, has steadily taken its toll and now drastically reduced the number of derelict mining sites that were once a common feature of the Cornish scene. This volume describes the surface remains of a further 214 mines to the names listed in my first book. Although the locations of a great many of these prospects are today identifiable only by a grassed-over burrow, the walls of a ruined building, or a solitary shaft, and in some cases are extremely difficult to find, they nevertheless represent the last traces left of a past generation of miners who, in their own way, helped to put Cornwall on the map as one of the greatest metalliferous regions of the Old World.

List of Plates

Bibliography and Acknowledgements

'Mines and Miners of Cornwall' 16 volumes   A.K.Hamilton-Jenkin
'The Metalliferous Mining Region of South West England'
Volumes 1 and 2   H.G.Dines
'Observations on the West of England Mining Region' J.H.Collins
'Wendron Tin'   A.K.Hamilton-Jenkin
'The Mining Journal' various copies Redruth Library Records

Thanks to Neil McKenna for additional research at Penzance Library and a great deal of footwork 'in the field'. Thanks also to many of the farmers throughout Cornwall who supplied relevant information and the whereabouts of particular workings, and co-operated in allowing me access to their land on which a large number of these mines now lie.

Councillor condemns Tehidy Park proposal

A PLAN to build a new visitor information centre in Tehidy Country Park has been condemned by a local councillor who says conversion of an existing building would be a better idea.

The county council intend to build the centre on the site of portable toilets at South Drive — council officials say the council officials say the centre will include new toilets which are desperately needed as the portable ones cannot cope with the number of visitors to the park.

The plan for new toilets is part of a number of improvements to facilities at the park which have been grouped together by the council in order to attract European funding.

Members of the county environment and community services committee heard last week that the improvements would also include renovating the Kennels to provide a camping barn and the building of a shower block for the school camping ground.

Local councillor Paul Holmes said the plan flew in the face of last week's decision by councillors at Kerrier to reject plans for homes at Tehidy. "Do we have 250 acres of woodland and then fill it up with buildings?" he asked.

An attempt should be made to convert an existing building, he said. The stable block would be a good choice if the Health Authority agreed to sell it.

However, committee chairman Barbara Spring said: "I am sure it would cost a considerable amount of money which we do not have."

West Penwith Peninsula

GREAT TREVAGEAN
D.   1837-1876
L.   1¾ miles N of Sennen Cove, on Nanquidno Downs SW369288
M/O. 20 tons tin
S.   The workings of this mine covered the area from Trevagean across to Nanquidno Downs, and the sett is identifiable today by one or two shafts and some gorse-covered burrows on the Downs south of Land's End Aerodrome.

CAER BRAN MINE
D.   Mid 1800's
L.   1 mile W of Sancreed SW404292
M/O. No records - tin
S.   Old gorse-covered burrows can be seen on the slopes of the hill above Caer Bran Farm, the only traces left from this unproductive tin trial.

WEST DING DONG
D.   circa 1850's
L.   ¾ mile NW of Sancreed SW416303
M/O. No records - tin
S.   The two surviving shafts of this little known tin mine, lying in fact a few miles south of the more famous Ding Dong, can be located south of Trannack Farm. One still remains open, near the Sancreed road, the other has been partly filled with rubble and is now covered in ferns and gorse.

WHEAL CUNNING
D.   1830-1876
L.   ½ mile W of St. Just SW362317
M/O. 460 tons tin
S.   The dumps of this mine, which also worked with nearby Boscean, are in a field slightly south of Bosweddon Road.

CARNYORTH
D.   1853-1860
L.   1 mile N of St. Just SW373333
M/O. 1,050 tons of tin before amalgamating with Botallack
S.   The scattered tips of Carnyorth are situated behind the village school, west of the B3306 St. Just road. The ruins of two buildings, one of which appears to be an old miner's dry, also stand on site.

WHEAL BAL

D.   1844-1865
L.   ½ mile NE of Carnyorth SW383336
M/O. A few tons of tin
S.   One of the less productive mines in the St. Just area, Wheal Bal's site today is marked by some overgrown dumps on Trewellard Common, at the top of Wheal Bal Hill.

DOLQUOTH (WHEAL ELIZABETH)

D.   1830-1868
L.   ¾ mile SE of Lower Drift SW452281
M/O. Some quantities of tin
S.   A single, fenced shaft situated beside a cabbage field near the Faugan Circle marks the site of this ancient prospect which was known to be in operation in the late 1700's.

WHEAL HENRY (WEST TOLVADDEN)

D.   1828-1863
L.   SE of Newlyn SW470279
M/O. 66 tons of copper
S.   Although all traces of this small copper mine in the vicinity of Penlee Quarry have now been obliterated, the drainage adit, with a brick archway, can be located on the low cliff opposite the quarry.

WHEAL SPERRIS AND SANDWICH

D.   1836-1850
L.   ¾ mile W of Towednack SW477380
M/O. No records - tin
S.   These mines were old, unproductive trials for tin in the moorland area between Zennor Hill and Towednack. A few gorse-covered dumps and the ruins of the mine's counthouse can be located in the rather bleak isolation of Beagletodn Downs.

GOOLE PELLAS

D.   1877-1881
L.   1 mile NE of Towednack SW499397
M/O. 526 tons tin
S.   The burrows of this mine, now much overgrown, lie just below the ruined engine houses of Rosewall and Ransom Mine, at the foot of Rosewall Hill.

VORVAS DOWNS AND BALNOON

D. 1837-1864, re-opened 1905
L. 1½ miles S of St. Ives SW513383 - SW508382
M/O. 213 tons tin
S. The extensive waste tips of theses two closely related setts can be seen in the vicinity of Higher Vorvas Farm, south of Halse Town.

HAWK'S POINT MINE

D. 1851-1870
L. Near Carbis Bay SW535388
M/O. 670 tons copper; 1 ton ochre; some tin
S. The main workings of this mine are located at Carrack Gladden Point, where there are some fairly cavernous levels and tunnels opening out near the beach, some of which are partly flooded with ochrous water. The portals of several other levels can be seen at the top of the cliff near the footpath. There is also another adit entrance further south of Hawk's Point.

WHEAL MERTH

D. 1852-1864
L. 1½ miles SW of Lelant SW524357
M/O. 755 tons tin
S. The mine was an amalgamation of several small tin prospects carrying out trials on Lelant Downs, amongst them Wheal Strawberry, South Wheal Kitty and Collurian Mine. Some grassed-over burrows and the portals of two adits adjoining the Canonstown stream are all that remain from this group.

Mount's Bay - Helston - Falmouth

WEST WHEAL FORTUNE

D. 1815-1891
L. 1¼ miles N of Marazion SW528326
M/O. 11,400 tons copper; 3,000 tons tin
S. The extensive waste tips of this mine, one of the more prosperous in the area, are still a conspicuous feature on the hillside north of the village of Truthwall

TOLVADDEN

D. 1857-1862
L. ½ mile E of Marazion SW531305
M/O. 10,750 tons copper; 12 tons tin
S. A large dump and a filled-in shaft can be located from this mine, near the junction of the A394 and B3280 roads on the outskirts of Marazion.

WHEAL NEPTUNE

D. 1811-1838
L. ¼ mile N of Perranuthnoe SW539300
M/O. 13,760 tons copper
S. This once rich mine lay to the east of the land leading to Perranuthnoe from the A394 road. Most of the dumps have now been removed, but some extensive tips and a shaft can be seen in the fields to the west of this lane.

TRENOW CONSOLS

D. 1845-1856
L. ¼ mile W of Perranuthnoe SW533297
M/O. 6,675 tons copper (as part of CHARLOTTE UNITED MINES)
S. One of a number of small copper producers on the cliffs south of Perranuthnoe, Trenow Consols site can be identified today by a single walled shaft in a corner of a field overlooking St. Michael's Mount and Mount's Bay.

WHEAL CHIVERTON AND TREVEAN

D. 1847-1865
L. ¾ mile E of Perranuthnoe SW549291
M/O. No records - copper
S. A filled-in shaft and some gorse-covered dumps remain from this unproductive mine, in the vicinity of Trevean Farm.

WHEAL CAROLINE

D. 1826-1832
L. ¼ mile SW of Goldsithney SW541305
M/O. 9,823 tons copper
S. Although abandoned so long ago, the remaining burrows of this mine, some of considerable size, can still be seen in fields to the east of the road leading into Goldsithney.

HALMANNING, CROFT AND RETALLACK

D.   1830-1858, re-worked 1912
L.   ½ mile E of St. Hilary SW565312
M/O. 23,420 tons copper
S.   These mines collectively exploited a large tract of land between Higher Downs and the River Hayle, and an extensive run of burrows and shafts testify to the amount of work carried out here.

WHEAL RIB

D.   1837-1847
L.   1 mile N of Porthleven SW623274
M/O. 263 tons of copper
S.   The site of this small copper mine is identifiable today by a solitary and now overgrown shaft burrow, on the valley side above the Porthleven stream. This can be best viewed from the A394 road near the Porthleven turning.

GREAT WHEAL FORTUNE

D.   1855-1880
L.   ½ mile W of Sithney SW626289
M/O. 2,992 tons tin; 322 tons copper; some wolfram and arsenic
S.   This mine worked on lodes in the valley near Trelissick and Carnmeal Downs. The shafts, dumps and dressing floors are to the east of the stream that runs through the valley, and are now partly hidden by encroaching undergrowth.

TREVENEN AND TREMENHERE

D.   1850-1870
L.. 2 miles NE of Helston SW679297 - SW684298
M/O. Several hundred tons of tin
S.   Two closely related setts that worked between Roselidden and Trevenen. Two large burrows in a field near Trevenen Bal still survive, with a gorse-covered shaft dump near the new housing estate a short distance east.

WHEAL UNITY

D.   1810-1845
L.   1 mile S of Mullion SW674173
M/O. No recorded output - copper
S.   Wheal Unity was an amalgamation of numerous small mining concerns

that worked on the moors to the south of Mullion, including Trenance Mine, Predannack Wartha and Wheal Foss. The portals of several adits belonging to this group can be located in the cliff face at Porth Pyg and the adjacent cove near Vro Rock, and some of these can be explored at low tide. The dumps, now mostly overgrown with gorse and ferns, can be seen at the above o/s reference and further south near Teneriffe (SW673167).

WHEAL VYVYAN
D. 1827-1864
L. ¼ mile N of Constantine SW734294
M/O. 8,477 tons copper; 92 tons tin
S. The area around the Helford Passage was not generally noted for any great mineral wealth, Wheal Vyvyan being the most productive mine, working copper lodes on high ground to the north of Constantine. The burrows remaining from these workings are still quite extensive and are a conspicuous feature above the village.

WHEAL ANNA MARIA
D. 1833-1860, re-worked 1907-1908
L. ½ mile NE of Porth Navas SW758282
M/O. 119 tons copper
S. The mine is situated in the steep wooded slopes between the road bridge at Porthnavas Creek and Lower Penpoll Farm. Old opencuts and overgrown dumps, with a few crumbling walls, are all that now remain.

WHEAL PENROSE
D. Unrecorded
L. Maenporth SW791298
M/O. No records - copper and lead
S. The single shaft of this mine which could formerly be found near the old coastguard station has now been filled but several short levels penetrating the low cliffs to the north of the beach can be explored in relative safety at low tide.

SILVER HILL
D. c.1830's
L. 1¼ miles W of Devoran SW778398
M/O. No records - lead
S. A small, insignificant venture working a lead lode to the west of Perranwell Station. A gorse covered dump in a field near the railway line is the only sign left of any mining activity in this area.

The St. Erth Valley

The St. Erth Valley through which the River Hayle flows was worked by a number of small ventures exploiting E - W lodes containing mostly copper and tin. To view what remains from these mines, it is best to commence a route from St. Erth village, heading in an easterly direction towards Praze and then in a clockwise direction to Relubbas, through Penberthy Cross to Trewinnard. A great deal of footwork is required to locate these workings which for the most part lie in small secluded valleys approached by narrow lanes.

Slightly south of St. Erth station is the sett of TRELOWETH MINE (SW541355). Active from 1812-1866, this mine produced nearly 6,500 tons of copper. A long, slaty burrow can be found in the field adjoining the road to the village. Opposite this, in the wood next to the field, the adit discharges water into a bog-filled trench which is dangerous to approach.

Plate 1: *Wheal Squire*

Half a mile out of St. Erth towards Praze, a lane forks south to Porthcollum. At SW557343, two large burrows in a field near Trenedros mark the site of WHEAL SQUIRE, which worked from 1817-1866, producing large quantities of copper. More burrows are to be seen in the vicinity of Trenedros Farm, on the eastern part of the Wheal Squire sett. This is probably the site of WHEAL

7

PENWITH, an insignificant venture that was abandoned in 1843.

To the east of Wheal Squire, a narrow track descends into a densely wooded valley. At the entrance to this trackway is a ruined building, partly clad in ivy. Between this relic and the stream are a line of old shaft burrows in the surrounding fields. These mark the site of CHYNOWETH MINE (SW564338) which was at work in the late 1800's but whose output is unrecorded.

Just over a ¼ mile east of this latter mine, the scattered waste tips of TREVEN MINE can be seen near the farm of the same name (SW572341). Worked from 1844-1873, copper and lead was produced here. Another grassed-over burrow can be seen east of Keskeys Farm at SW581340.

South of Treven, in another wooded valley, is the sett of WHEAL NUT (SW575334). The burrows of this mine, also known as LEWIS MINE, now lie hidden in dense undergrowth, as do the workings of WHEAL TULE, which is situated a short distance south at SW573328. Wheal Nut ceased operations in the 1860's, producing 1,275 tons of tin, whilst Wheal Tule was an unsuccessful trial commenced in 1907, and abandoned soon after.

To the west of Wheal Tule, more overgrown burrows in a field south of Trannack mark the site of GURLYN (SW563327), worked from 1860-1865 and re-opened in 1904, producing 475 tons of copper and 180 tons of tin. On a direct line west, another group of old dumps in fields near Ennys belong to ENNYS WHEAL VIRGIN (SW562324), active in the 1840's on a very limited scale.

WHEAL FRIENDSHIP (SW555316), whose extensive but now gorse-covered dumps are a conspicuous feature in the area bordering Kestal Farm, was in operation from 1810-1863, producing 11,000 tons of copper, and some quantities of tin. Northwards of this mine, at SW554325, PENBERTHY CROFTS was in operation in the late 1800's and worked spasmodically up to 1883, producing 8,700 tons of copper and some lead and tin. The burrows from this mine still lie in the fields on either side of the road leading to St. Erth.

A short distance north east of Trewinnard, WHEAL ELIZABETH worked on the western extension of the Wheal Squire copper lodes, on a more limited scale. Active from 1831-1834, 4,600 tons of copper was produced here. A slatey shaft burrow on the bank of the River Hayle, near the bridge, is the only remaining feature of this mine (SW548341).

8

Leedstown - Wendron

WEST PROVIDENCE
D. 1851-1883
L. West of Fraddam SW587346
M/O. 11,535 tons copper; 790 tons tin
S. The extensive waste tips of this copper mine can be seen on either side of the road from Fraddam to Praze.

WHEAL GODOLPHIN
D. 1815-1850
L. ¾ mile SE of Townshend SW602324
M/O. 9,800 tons copper; 10 tons tin
S. Lying below Godolphin Hill in a shallow valley, Wheal Godolphin's long line of burrows and sand piles are now mostly overgrown with gorse and can be located to the east of the bridge.

BINNER DOWNS
D. 1819-1838
L. ½ mile SE of Leedstown SW613338
M/O. 51,000 tons copper
S. The widespread dumps and shafts of this old and rich copper producer still cover the fields east of the B3302 road south of Leedstown.

CRENVER AND WHEAL ABRAHAM
D. 1815-1870
L. 1¼ miles E of Leedstown SW625339
M/O. 112,000 tons copper
S. Another rich copper mine in this highly mineralised area, whose numerous dumps, burrows and shafts litter the countryside between Leedstown and the B3303 road near Crenver Grove.

WHEAL TREMAYNE AND WHEAL TREASURY
D. 1815-1870
L. North and north east of Leedstown SW606348-SW612344
M/O. 12,00 tons copper; 1,490 tons tin
S. Two closely related setts whose extensive shafts and dumps can be seen on Gwinear Downs and Burnt Downs.

9

ROSEWARNE CONSOLS

D.   1858-1869
L.   1¼ miles E of Gwinear SW621362
M/O. 2,950 tons copper
S.   The scattered dumps of this mine can still be traced in fields between Bosparva, Cathebedron Cross and Rosewarne village.

WHEAL LAMIN (NORTH UNITY)

D.   circa 1850's
L.   1 mile N of Leedstown SW606358
M/O. 162 tons copper
S.   One of the less productive mines in this area, Lamin's site still exhibits the remains of two burrows in a field south of Lamin Farm.

TRENOWETH

D.   1814-1822
L.   ½ mile SW of Crowan SW638342
M/O. 4,976 tons copper
S.   Even after being abandoned so long ago, the site of this ancient copper mine can still be identified today by a large but now much overgrown burrow in a field facing the wall that surrounds Clowance Park, beside the B3303 road.

OATFIELD

D.   circa 1840's
L.   ¾ mile SW of Crowan SW638338
M/O. Included with Crenver and Abraham Mine
S.   Two open shafts and some fairly extensive waste tips can be seen to the east of the B3303 road, and south of Trenoweth. The mine worked on the eastern extensions of the Crenver and Abraham copper lodes, with limited results.

RELEATH (CROWAN AND WENDRON CONSOLS)

D.   1851-1865
L.   1¼ miles NW of Wendron SW668329
M/O. No records - copper
S.   Although covering a wide area, this mine was a poor producer of copper. A few grassed-over burrows can still be located on high ground to the east of Lower Releath.

WHEAL LAMB, WHEAL VRAWZ AND PROSPIDINICK

South of Releath Mine, near the bend in the road to Longstone Down at SW658325, a trackway heads in a south westerly direction over the Downs. The remains of these old, unproductive tine mines can be found in the vicinity of this path. In a corner of a field at SW654323 are the scattered dumps of WHEAL LAMB. Although at work in the early 1800's, there are no records of any output from this concern. The site of WHEAL VRAWZ is today marked by a grassed-over mound near the Men-amber logan stone (SW646319). This long forgotten venture was little more than a trial on these Downs. More extensive remains can be seen at PROSPIDINICK MINE (SW643315) where a line of waste tips are situated in fields slightly west of the railway line. This mine produced some quantities of tin and was abandoned in the 1860's.

TREVARNO

D.   1840-1848
L.   1 mile S of Nancegollan SW645305
M/O. A few tons of copper and tin
S.   Although at work in the late 18th. century, few records exist of this mine which still exhibits a few overgrown burrows west of the railway.

WHEAL CRUETT

D.   Early 1800's - 1865
L.   ¼ mile SW of Nancegollan SW628313
M/O. No records - tin
S.   This mine worked on the eastern extensions of the Polladras Downs lodes with little success, also under the name of NORTH WHEAL METAL. At the edge of a field adjoining the B3302 road west of Little Pengwedna is a walled shaft of large dimensions, together with a grassed-over slatey mound, the only traces now left of this mine.

WHEAL HENRY

D.   1839-1842
L.   ½ mile SE of Wendron SW687305
M/O. No records - tin
S.   A few scattered tips north of Crahan Farm are all that remain from this unproductive tin mine.

EAST BASSET AND GRYLS

D.   circa 1850's
L.   East of Porkellis SW696333
M/O. No records - an unproductive trial for tin

S.   A single shaft near the lane from Porkellis church to Lower Porkellis marks the site of this small, obscure trial.

POLHIGEY MOOR AND POLHIGEY
D.   1862-1873, re-worked 1926-1928
L.   1¼ miles NE of Porkellis SW705352
M/O. Small quantities of tin
S.   These two mines worked on lodes in the rather bleak moorland area between Penmarth and Halabezack. Most of the workings south of Halabezack have now been ploughed over, but some shafts and a few dumps can be seen to the east of the road leading into Penmarth.

Hayle - Camborne

MELLANEAR
D.   1815-1888
L.   ¾ mile S of Hayle SW561362
M/O. 66,400 tons copper; 80 tons tin
S.   Some old dumps from this once rich copper producer still lie in a field to the east of the B3302 road into Hayle.

WHEAL ANN (WEST ALFRED CONSOLS)
D.   1805-1865
L.   ¾ mile SE of Hayle SW566364
M/O. 9,100 tons copper; some lead
S.   A few remaining burrows can be seen south of Halankene from one of the numerous mines in this area that incorporated the name 'Alfred' in their title.

NORTH WHEAL ALFRED
D.   circa 1840's
L.   ½ mile E of Hayle SW572374
M/O. No recorded output - copper
S.   One of the least productive and lesser known of the Alfred.Mines, this sett is identifiable today by a large overgrown burrow beside the road east of High Lanes.

WHEAL ALFRED AND ALFRED CONSOLS

D.   1801-1864
L.   East of Hayle SW578371 - SW589370
M/O. 175,000 tons copper
S.   This group of mines were the most productive in the area, working the shallow valley between Wheal Alfred and Gwinear. The extensive burrows of Alfred Consols are still a conspicuous part of the landscape to the south west of Gwinear, whilst Wheal Alfred's site exhibits only a few scattered tips near Treglistian.

TREVASCUS

D.   1837-1842
L.   ½ mile NW of Carnhell Green SW611380
M/O. 1,190 tons copper; 110 tons tin
S.   A shaft and some gorse-covered burrows exist on the site, north of Trenoweth Farm.

RELISTIEN

D.   1832-1851
L.   ¾ mile SW of Carnhell Green SW604368
M/O. 12,150 tons copper
S.   This mine was originally worked by open trenches and excavations, and later by shafts. A few undulations in the ground near Wall date from early years of production, in the 18th. century, whilst several shaft dumps on both sides of the road north from Wall are from the later period.

PENDARVES AND ST. AUBYN CONSOLS

D.   1815-1858
L.   East of Carnhell Green SW623375
M/O. 7,635 tons copper; some tin
S.   Included in this group were East Rosewarne and Wheal Duffield, working copper lodes on Penhale Moor. One open shaft and a line of old burrows can be seen to the south of the road between Weeth and Carnhell Green.

NORTH DOLCOATH

D.   1857-1862, re-opened 1910-1914
L.   North of Barripper SW634385
M/O. Quantities of copper, tin, wolfram and silver
S.   The site of this old unproductive mine, named hopefully after Dolcoath,

lies in thickets to the west of Barripper school, down a small trackway. Some overgrown dumps and a few walls are all that remain.

WEST STRAY PARK
D.   1850-1874
L.   ½ mile E of Penponds SW646392
M/O. 3,655 tons copper
S.   The burrows of this mine, which worked on the extensions of the Stray Park lodes, can be located in the fields to the north of the Kellivose-Camborne Beacon slip road.

TRYPHENA
D.   1847-1863
L.   ¾ mile SE of Penponds SW647388
M/O. Quantities of copper and tin
S.   Later incorporated into the Pendarves United sett, Tryphena's dumps are located at the edge of a wood east of Kellivose.

TOLCARNE AND SOUTH TOLCARNE
D.   1860-1883
L.   ½ mile NW of Troon, near Camborne Beacon SW655388
M/O. 6,930 tons copper
S.   The widespread dumps and shafts of these two mines cover nearly the whole of the hillside below Camborne Beacon, between Tolcarne and Knave-go-By.

FOREST MINE
D.   circa 1850's
L.   1 mile SE of Troon SW676378
M/O. No records - trials for tin and copper
S.   Few records exist concerning this small mine that carried out trials for copper and tin near Bolenowe Moor. Nevertheless, two fairly large burrows still survive from this working, lying on the eastern bank of the Bolenowe stream, below Forest Farm.

BOLENOWE (SOUTH WHEAL GRENVILLE)
D.   1821-1870
L.   ½ mile E of Troon SW668382
M/O. 138 tons copper

S.   The overgrown dumps of this very small copper producer can be seen near the road from Bolenowe to Troon. The ruins of an old building, possibly a miner's dry or cottage, also survive on the site.

Plate 2: *Polgear and Lancarrow*

POLGEAR AND LANCARROW

D.   circa 1850's
L.   ¾ mile S of Four Lanes SW687375
M/O. Small amounts of tin
S.   A few scattered dumps and mounds are in fields to the east of the B3297 road, the last traces of this long-forgotten prospect. A ruined building of quite substantial size is also on the site, at Polgear hamlet. Part of this structure was being renovated in 1988.

BULLER AND BASSET UNITED

D.   1850-1864
L.   ¼ mile NE of Four Lanes SW695388
M/O. No records - tin and copper
S.   The burrows of this old and unprofitable mine are still visible in fields to the north east of Four Lanes church.

WHEAL ROME (WEST ROSKEAR)

D. 1830-1879
L. ¾ mile W of Camborne SW623403
M/O. Small quantities of lead and copper
S. The mine is situated near the junction of the A.30 road and the new by-pass west of Treswithian Farm. Two walled shafts and some extensive tips still remains, despite road reconstruction in this area.

WHEAL JOHNNY (NORTH SETON) AND VIOLET SETON

D. 1862-1887
L. 1¼ miles NW of Camborne SW627413 - SW632414
M/O. 1,270 tons copper
S. These two closely related setts worked on Treswithian Downs near Kehelland, where a few dumps and one or two shafts can be seen today.

WHEAL PROSPER

D. 1812-1837
L. 3¼ miles W of Camborne SW588406
M/O. No records - copper
S. The still surviving burrows of this old and unproductive mine are grouped in a field to the west of Prosper Hill near Gwithian.

WHEAL ST. ANDREW

D. 1836-1861
L. 3 miles W of Camborne SW595402
M/O. 1,673 tons copper
S. Although lying a short distance south east of Wheal Prosper, this mine was far more productive, as can be seen from the size of the remaining burrows east of Gwithian Road, at the top of Prosper Hill.

Redruth - St. Day - Chacewater

WHEAL MARY

D. 1827-1873
L. ¾ mile N of Redruth SW693433
M/O. 7,670 tons copper; 184 tons tin
S. Situated to the east of the Portreath road, near the by-pass flyover,

Wheal Mary's overgrown dumps can still be located on the hillside at Gilbert's Coombe.

SOUTH CARN BREA
D.   1858-1889
L.   1¼ miles SW of Redruth SW688408
M/O.   22,000 tons copper
S.   A large burrow from this mine can be seen on the eastern slope of Carn Brea. below the hillside, beside the footpath to Carnkie, is a fairly cavernous system of levels which can be explored in relative safety.

EAST WHEAL UNY (BUCKETS)
D.   1846-1850
L.   ½ mile S of Redruth SW702412
M/O.   2,700 tons copper
S.   A very large dump and a shaft survive from this small copper producer, near the junction of the Helston-Redruth roads.

Eastwards of Redruth, numerous copper mines worked on the north and eastern slopes of Carn Marth, and flourished in and around the highly mineralised zones of St. Day and Caharrack. The first such mine leaving Redruth towards St. Day is WHEAL ST. AUBYN (SW712418), worked in close conjunction with WHEAL GRAMBLA whose ivy-covered engine house stands near Ninnis. There are some extensive waste tips and several shafts remaining from this mine which was in operation from 1871-1893. To the north of the Redruth-St. Day road, a few grassed-over mounds and burrows in the fields beside the footpath to North Trefula mark the site of the combined WHEAL CUPID, WHEAL LILY and WHEAL TREFULA (SW717425), small copper ventures at work in the 1850's and 1860's. Nearer to St. Day village are the workings of TOLCARNE, also known as WEST JEWELL and NORTH WHEAL DAMSEL (SW725422). Between 1831 and 1854, this mine produced 13,000 tons of copper. The remaining dumps, shafts and burrows are still a conspicuous feature of the countryside to the west of the village, and the portals of two adits can be located near the Tolcarne stream.

To the east of St. Day are the rapidly diminishing waste tips of WHEAL GORLAND, at the bottom of Telegraph Hill (SW734426). This was in operation from 1850-1860 and re-worked in the early part of this century. Subsidences caused by the underground levels of this mine have occurred in St. Day quite frequently over the past few years.

In dense woodland to the north of Trefula Farm, two large dumps mark the sett of WHEAL PINK (SW724427). This was worked from 1815-1850 and produced moderate quantities of copper. At one stage, Wheal Pink was also working in conjunction with Wheal Gorland.

Near Little Caharrack are another set of burrows and shafts that have changed little in appearance over the past two decades. This is the site of WHEAL DAMSEL (SW728417), a copper producer worked from 1815-1872 producing 37,000 tons of ore. A mountainous shaft burrow further south on the slope of Carn Marth indicates the site of the equally productive WEST DAMSEL (SW725410), which produced 29,150 tons of copper between 1852-1874. WHEAL JEWELL has waste tips and some extremely deep and cavernous open mine shafts beside the St. Day-Caharrack road, and in the area around Crofthandy. 58,150 tons of copper was recorded here from 1815-1853 (SW735422).

WHEAL MAID (ALSO CAHARRACK AND EAST DAMSEL)
D.   1821-1880, re-opened 1935-1939
L.   East of Caharrack SW741418
M/O.   27,800 tons copper
S.   The numerous dumps, shafts and burrows of these mines still litter the landscape between Caharrack and the western slopes of United Downs. The walls of a few ruined buildings are also on the site. Part of Wheal Maid's workings are today being utilised by Wheal Jane Mine.

CREEGBRAWSE AND PENKEVIL
D.   1815-1869
L.   1 mile NE of St. Day SW746435
M/O.   16,500 tons copper; 1,320 tons tin; 50 tons arsenic
S.   The only feature remaining from this mine today is a large waste tip on the hillside above Todpool village beside the road to Twelveheads.

TING TANG (WEST CLIFFORD UNITED)
D.   1816-1865
L.   ¼ mile S of Caharrack SW730409
M/O.   40,000 tons copper
S.   A shaft and some scattered waste tips remain from this once prosperous mine, at the northern boundary of Outer Wood, west of the B3298 road into Caharrack.

WHEAL SQUIRE
D.   1816-1853
L.   ½ mile SE of Caharrack SW738409
M/O.   20,000 tons copper

S.   A few overgrown shafts, some walls and old burrows can still be located in Outer Wood, to the south of Sparry Bottom.

EAST WHEAL FALMOUTH
D.   1835-1865
L.   1¼ miles NE of Twelveheads SW780429
M/O. 47 tons copper; 413 tons lead; 17,000 oz silver
S.   Part of the Falmouth Consolidated Mines group, the bracken-covered waste tips of this small copper producer still survive in fields on the outskirts of Treva Farm.

WHEAL JANE
L.   1½ miles NE of Twelveheads
S.   The original Wheal Jane workings lay to the north of the new complex, between Hugus and Carrine Common, and this area is still scarred with the burrows and shafts remaining from these earlier operations. The most impressive artifacts left from the 'old men' are the cavernous excavations beside the track from Goodern to Chygoose Farm (SW786432), where the ore was quarried in ancient times. Although these chasm-like trenches are now partly obscured by trees and lined with undergrowth, it is still an eerie experience today to look down into these dark, seemingly bottomless pits which are quite dangerous to approach. The well preserved power house, built in 1907, stands a short distance to the west of Goodern Farm.

SOUTH TRESAVEAN
D.   1860-1870, re-opened 1912
L.   NE of Ponsanooth SW761378
M/O. No records - silver and uranium
S.   The main adit of this mine, which was explored by the Atomic Energy Authority in the late 1950's because of the presence of uranium in this area, has its portal at the foot of a quarry to the left of the footpath leading from the dis-used mill to the old railway. The remainder of the workings now lie in dense undergrowth in woods adjoining the path.

MAGDALEN MINE
D.   Intermittently worked in the 1800's, re-worked 1913-1929
L.   East of Ponsanooth SW765377
M/O. Quantities of tin
S.   A mine with a long history dating back to the 17th. century, with very little success as regards production of tin. The adits, opencuts and other

ruins lie in woodland adjacent to the slip road from the village to the main A39 Truro road, and undergrowth covers most of this mine from view.

WHEAL DANIELL

D. C.1870's
L. ½ mile NW of Chacewater SW749449
M/O. No recorded output - copper and ochre
S. The much overgrown dumps of this unproductive mine can be seen to the south of the road from Chacewater to Blackwater.

Plate 3 *Carnhot mine*

NORTH WHEAL BUSY (CARNHOT)

D. 1830-1860
L. 1¼ miles NW Chacewater SW735457
M/O. No records- copper
S. Few records exist regarding this mine which was in operation in the early part of the 19th century as Carnhot and Killiwerris. This is surprising as the numerous shafts and dumps, with their traditional granite walls, are the most extensive in this area, lying in the fields on both sides of the Blackwater - Chacewater road and also adjacent to the abandoned railway line. The mine was undoubtedly working on the extensions of the Great Wheal Busy lodes with less success than that famous copper producer.

Scorrier - St. Agnes - Perranporth

WHEAL CONCORD

D. 1823-1868, recently re-opened

L. ½ mile W of Blackwater SW728461

M/O. Quantities of tin

S. Some exploratory work has been carried out at Wheal Concord in recent years, but the mine has once again been abandoned because of poor results. A small wooden headframe stands over the main shaft, a legacy of this small latter activity and a conspicuous object near Skinner's Bottom.

Plate 4: *Wheal Concord*

STENCOOSE AND MAWLA

D. circa 1860's, re-worked 1912 and 1927

L. 1¼ miles NW of Scorrier SW713459

M/O. No recorded output - copper

S. A solitary walled shaft and some scanty burrows remain from this unproductive copper mine, near the junction of the Scorrier-Two Burrows road, north of Stencoose Farm.

SOUTH ELLEN

D. 1856-1861

L. 1¼ miles E of Porthtowan SW707466

M/O. 2,600 tons copper; some lead and zinc

S. The widespread waste tips and shafts of this mine are a conspicuous feature on the hillside to the west of the road opposite to Menagissey Farm. Good mineral specimens can be collected from the dumps in this area.

VICTORIA MINE

D.   circa 1850's

L.   1 mile W of Blackwater SW720467

M/O. No records - copper

S.   An old, little known copper venture whose sett can still be identified today by three overgrown shaft burrows in a field to the west of Coosewartha Farm, near Mount Hawke.

Plate 5: *Trenethick mine*

TRENETHICK MINE

D.   1800-1806, re-worked 1870's

L.   1¼ miles SE of Goonvrea SW718479

M/O. Small amounts of copper

S.   This is another very old prospect in this area, few records of which exist. The site, however, can still be located today by some fairly extensive burrows lying in fields to the south of Gover Farm, on the outskirts of Mount Hawke.

WHEAL DUCHY

D.   circa 1830's

L.   1 mile SE of Goonvrea SW718486

M/O. No records - included with WHEAL TOWAN

S.   This small prospect worked on the eastern extensions of the Wheal Towan copper lodes with very limited results. A single, gorse-covered burrow still survives in a field to the south east of Mingoose Farm, the only surface remains left.

BEVAS MOOR (OLD EAST TYWARNHAYLE)
D.   1835-1847
L.   ½ mile S of Goonbell SW732490
M/O. Small amounts of copper
S.   A mine on the western part of the sett of Burrow and Butson, worked spasmodically under a variety of names with limited results. Some scattered waste tips west of Wheal Butson Farm still remain on the site.

WHEAL BURROW AND BUTSON
D.   1837-1876
L.   ¾ mile SE of Goonbell SW738491
M/O. 1,300 tons copper; 893 tons zinc; 50 tons lead
S.   First worked under the name of Wheal Davey, this was one of the more prosperous mines in the area, as can be seen from the still surviving burrows and shafts which cover the fields in the vicinity of Wheal Butson and Wheal Davey Farms.

SILVERWELL (WHEAL TREASURE)
D.   Re-worked early part of this century
L.   ¾ mile E of Wheal Burrow and Butson Mine SW749487
M/O. Quantities of lead
S.   This mine, prospected several times over the last century with very little success, is today situated in swampy undergrowth and thickets beside the Perran Combe stream near the ford. Two shafts and a mountainous dump can still be located at this site.

PERRAN WHEAL VIRGIN
D.   1845-1874
L.   1¼ miles E of Silverwell SW772492
M/O. Small quantities of copper, lead and silver
S.   A few grassed-over burrows survive from this mine, in a circular copse of trees to the south east of Callestick Vean.

WENTWORTH CONSOLS

D.   1855-1867
L.   1 mile NE of Callestick SW787512
M/O. No records - lead
S.   Although few records exist of this lead producer, some extensive burrows and dumps remain on the site. Also to be seen are the foundation walls of the mine's chimney stack, which was blown-up in the 1950's. The blocks of stone resulting from this demolition are scattered in the corner of a field to the north west of West Chiverton Mine.

NORTH CHIVERTON

D.   1863-1868
L.   ½ mile S of Goonhavern SW788530
M/O. 100 tons lead; 3,640 oz silver; 630 tons zinc
S.   One of the less productive of the Chiverton group of mines, North Chiverton's surviving burrows can still be seen to the west of the road into Goonhavern, south of Eden Farm.

Plate 6: *Wheal Albert*

WHEAL ALBERT (GOONHAVERN MINE)

D.   1852-1867
L.   ½ mile E of Goonhavern SW796536
M/O. Quantities of lead and silver

S. The dumps of this mine, now mostly covered in gorse, extend in an unbroken line from Penrose Farm to Little Water Farm, north of the B3285 road. Standing in a field to the north of the latter farm, adjacent to a small bridge crossing the abandoned railway line, are the remains of Wheal Albert's pumping engine house, now in ruins with the chimney stack missing. Some fresher dumps containing a few mineral specimens can be found in the vicinity of this relic.

PERRAN GREAT ST. GEORGE AND DROSKYN

D.　1815-1899
L.　½ mile SW of Perranporth SW745536
M/O.　106,000 tons copper; quantities of lead, zinc, tins and wolfram
S.　The numerous shafts and waste tips of this once rich group of copper producers are still a conspicuous feature of the landscape to the west of the road leading out of Perranporth towards Trevellas.

PENHALE, WHEAL GOLDEN AND GRAVEL HILL

L.　North of Perran Beach, between Ligger and Penhale Point

S.　The excavations, dumps, shafts and adits of this group of lead and copper producers scar the headlands and cliffs to the west of Holywell (SW758580-SW760591). The Perran Iron Lode, worked by a host of mines eastward of the cliffs, commences at Gravel Hill Mine where a spectacular man-made cavern and lagoon, with a system of small tunnels, is at the base of the cliffs at SW764576. Most of the shafts which border on Ministry of Defence property, are now fenced and capped. The several engine houses that once stood on these cliffs have all now been demolished.

Plate 7: *Cliff workings - Gravel Hill*

25

Newlyn East - St. Austell

TREREW
D.   1844-1870
L.   1½ miles NW of Newlyn East SW812584
M/O. No records - lead
S.   A grassed-over burrow in a field to the north of Trerew Farm on high ground marks the site of this small lead mine. A very old building partly in ruins associated with this prospect also stands on the site, south of the farm.

DEERPARK
D.   1875-1879
L.   1¼ miles W of Newlyn East SW808555
M/O. Quantities of lead and iron
S.   This mine worked on the furthest eastern extensions of the Great Perran Iron Lode, with limited results. A few dumps and pits are the only traces now left, in fields near the long abandoned Shepherds branch railway line.

WHEAL ACLAND
D.   circa 1840's
L.   ½ mile NE of Newlyn East SW833572
M/O. No records - lead
S.   Little more than a trial for lead on a presumed extension of one of the East Wheal Rose lodes, the site of this mine is still identifiable today by some small, overgrown dumps in a wood adjoining Trendrean Farm.

SHEPHERDS MINE (OLD SHEPHERDS)
D.   1853-1885
L.   1½ miles S of Newlyn East SW818541
M/O. 430 tons lead; 3,600 oz silver; 175 tons zinc
S.   The widespread burrows and shafts of this mine are scattered over the countryside between the abandoned railway line and the road to Fiddler's Green.

EAST CHIVERTON

D.   1862-1883

L.   ¾ mile W of Zelah SW801515

M/O. 350 tons lead; 4,080 oz silver

S.   An unproductive mine working on the eastern extensions of the Wheal
     Chiverton lodes, East Chiverton's overgrown dumps and shafts lie in
     woods on the northern boundary of the Merton Plantation.

PENCORSE CONSOLS

D.   1842-1859

L.   1 mile NE of Mitchell SW870558

M/O. 15 tons lead; quantities of silver, zinc and blende

S.   The few scattered waste tips of this mine can still be located in fields to
     the north east of Trevessa Farm.

WHEAL ENNIS

D.   1851-1853

L.   1¾ miles NE of Zelah SW836533

M/O. No records - trials for lead

S.   This obscure and unprofitable lead trial can still, surprisingly, be
     identified today by a fairly large burrow in a corn field to the south of
     the A30 road near Higher Ennis Farm. About ¾ mile to the south west
     of this mine, two more burrows can be seen at SW824524, indication of
     further trials for lead in the area north of St. Allen.

Plate 8: *East Wheal Elizabeth*

27

EAST WHEAL ELIZABETH (GREAT CHIVERTON CONSOLS)

D.   1830-1870

L.   ¼ mile N of St. Allen SW820512

M/O. Only 81 tons of copper recorded

S.   Although this mine is only credited with having produced a few tons of copper, a great deal more work must have been carried out at this site, as the numerous burrows and shafts covering the hillside to the north of St. Allen indicate a considerable amount of underground activity in this area.

Plate 9: *Tin Hill*

TIN HILL (CARLOGGAS)

D.   1869-1881

L.   1 mile N of Gwindra SW958543

M/O. 4 tons tin

S.   The ivy-covered remains of the 24" pumping engine house, reduced to the lower walls through demolition, still stand on the site of this small and unprofitable mine. This relic, together with a fenced shaft, is situated in a corner of a field to the north east of Carloggas hamlet, and overlooks the china clay tips near St. Austell.

Plate 10: *Terras Mine*

TERRAS

D.   1870-1884

L.   ¾ mile W of St. Stephen SW933528

M/O. Small quantities of tin

S.   The well-preserved engine house of this small tin producer now stands on private ground to the east of the road into St. Stephen - marked 'Terras Mine Cottages' on the O/S maps.

SOUTH TERRAS

D.   1873-1910, re-worked up to 1923

L.   1 mile SW of St. Stephen SW935523

M/O. 736 tons uranium; 5,423 tons iron; 760 tons ochre

S.   The dumps of this interesting mine which exploited both iron and uranium lodes are now mostly overgrown and are situated in wood to the south east of Tolgarrick Mill. A tall, well preserved chimney stack still survives on the site, standing at the edge of a wood north of the mill in the Fal Valley

Plate 11: *South Terras*

29

WHEAL LOUISA
D. 1846-1869
L. ¾ mile SW of St. Stephen's Coombe SW942508
M/O. No records - lead
S. A solitary overgrown shaft and an opencut can be located from this old sett, in dense woodland beside the road to the south east of Crow Hill.

WHEAL LADY GRENVILLE
D. circa 1860's
L. ¾ mile S of St. Stephen's Coombe SW952505
M/O. No records - lead and copper
S. Most of the burrows of this mine have been removed in recent years, but a single, walled shaft remains, in a field to the north of Harvose Farm.

WHEAL FORTESCUE
D. 1864-1880
L. ¼ mile SE of St. Stephen's Coombe SW955513
M/O. 15 tons tin
S. Some grassed-over mounds in a field to the west of the road leading into the village remain, together with the granite walls of an associated building.

PENGELLY
D. 1818-1845
L. 1¼ miles SE of Hewas Water SW979483
M/O. No records - nickel
S. The workings of this mine, which today consist of a few pits and an overgrown dump, lie in dense woodland adjacent to the stream that flows south of Pengelly Farm. A track in the fields opposite to the woods is the best way to reach this secluded prospect.

PARK MATHEWS
D. circa 1820's
L. 1 mile E of London Apprentice SX024501
M/O. No records - copper and tin
S. Although this small mine was abandoned so long ago, two overgrown dumps still survive on the property. These can be seen on either side of the footpath near the cottages in Park Mathews Wood, most of which is now private property.

WHEAL NEPTUNE

D.   1812-1821
L.   ½ mile SE of Higher Porthpean SX032496
M/O. No records - copper
S.   A long forgotten trial for copper on the cliffs east of Castle Gotha Farm. A small overgrown burrow near Silvermine Point is the sole reminder of any mining activity in this area.

WHEAL POLMEAR AND SOUTH POLMEAR

D.   1856-1900
L.   ¼ mile SE of St. Austell SX035518
M/O. 6,490 tons copper; also quantities of zinc and lead
S.   The main workings of this group, which produced a wide variety of ores in moderate quantities, are situated in woods to the north of the Duporth road and west of Charlestown. There are also some extensive waste tips near the junction of the road at SX030515.

CRINNIS AND WEST CRINNIS

D.   1815-1881
L.   1¼ miles E of St. Austell SX050523-SX062524
M/O. 44,240 tons copper; quantities of silver and pyrites
S.   These mines collectively worked on copper lodes on the coastal strip of land between Crinnis Wood and Carlyon Bay. The dumps and shafts of Crinnis are still a feature on the edge of the golf course which now forms most of the bay inland from the railway line. These dumps are particularly extensive at SX054525. More remains can be found a short distance west in Crinnis Wood.

BOSCUNDLE

D.   1851-1864
L.   1¼ miles E of St. Austell SX047532
M/O. 1,115 tons tin; 205 tons copper
S.   In later years, up to the beginning of this century, this mine worked with the Eliza Consols group whose sett lay immediately to the west. Two large burrows and a collapsed shaft, now fenced, can be seen in a field to the west of the road from the A390 to Tregrehan Mills. The Eliza Consols group, including the ruined engine house and chimney stack of Tregrehan Consols Mine, are in woods on higher ground near the Boscundle workings.

MENABILLY WHEAL RASHLEIGH

D. circa 1850's
L. 1 mile SE of Par SX088526
M/O. No records - copper
S. This somewhat obscure and little known prospect, which was at work on a presumed eastern extension of the Crinnis copper lode, can still be identified today by its adit, the portal of which can be located on the low cliffline at Little Hell Cove, below Trill Farm.

WHEAL HOWELL

D. circa 1830's
L. ¼ mile W of Lansallos SX168518
M/O. No records - copper
S. A single overgrown dump and a shaft hidden by gorse survive from this old, unproductive sett. These can be found near the valley bottom and adjacent to the stream, south of Trevarder Farm.

WHEAL FORTESCUE (SILVER VEIN)

D. 1855-1868
L. 1¼ miles E of Lostwithiel SX122597
M/O. Small quantities of silver, lead and copper
S. Not to be confused with Wheal Fortescue near St. Stephen's Coombe, this mine exploited a silver-lead lode on high ground at Beacon Hill. The remains to be seen near the summit of this hill today consist of two very large dumps now covered in gorse, together with the stump of the mine's chimney stack. The site is best reached from the east, by taking the road to Trewether and proceeding over the hill from SX125595.

NORTH FORTESCUE

D. circa 1870's
L. 1½ miles NE of Lostwithiel SX123606
M/O. No records - lead
S. This small mine worked on the extensions of the Wheal Fortescue lodes with limited results. Some overgrown burrows and undulations in the woods and fields to the south of Hartwell Marsh Farm are all that remain.

Newquay - Wadebridge

CHIVERTON WHEAL ROSE
D.   1862-1864
L.   Near Pentire, Newquay SW802611
M/O. No records - lead
S.   The adit of this small lead prospect is on the north bank of the Gannel below Trethellan, although a thick tangle of undergrowth hides the entrance from view. The remainder of the workings now lie buried under the new housing estate.

WHEAL PROVIDENCE (NEWQUAY CONSOLS)
D.   1847-1860
L.   Near Fistral Beach, Newquay SW801619
M/O. A few tons of lead
S.   Another small lead producer in this area whose site can be identified today by a grassed-over burrow beside the footpath that crosses the golf course at Fristral Bay.

Plate 12: *Trewollack*

TREWOLLACK
D.   1845-1870
L.   ¾ mile SE of St. Columb Minor SW849615
M/O. No records - lead

33

S.   Trewollack was one of a number of small prospects carrying out trials for lead and copper in the area between St. Columb Minor and Quintral Downs, most of which had been abandoned by the 1870's. The small but well preserved chimney stack of Trewollack, with a distinctive square stone base, is the only mining relic left to be seen in this area. This stands in a corner of a field to the north of the farm of the same name, and south of Rialton Barton.

NORTH GREAT TRELETHER

D.   1857-1862
L.   1 mile N of Padstow SW912768
M/O. No records - copper
S.   A small, insignificant venture prospecting for copper near Harbour Cove, north of Tregirls Farm. The portal of the adit can still be seen today, in the low bank of the cove near the coastal footpath.

WHEAL JUBILEE

D.   1810-1820
L.   ½ mile W of Padstow SW905750
M/O. Small quantities of copper
S.   A very old and long forgotten copper mine whose site can still be identified today by an overgrown mound of waste material in a field to the south of Treator hamlet.

CREDIS MINE

D.   1822-1870
L.   1¼ miles S of Padstow SW913731
M/O. Quantities of copper
S.   One of the more prosperous of the many of the smaller copper mines in the Padstow area, the dumps of Credis are now overgrown and lie in fields above Little Petherick Creek.

LEGOSSICK

D.   1816-1830
L.   1¼ miles NE of St. Issey SW947725
M/O. 366 tons copper
S.   The overgrown dumps and the base walls of an old building still survive from this sett, which was known to be in operation in the 16th. century. These remains lie at the edge of a steeply sloping field overlooking Pinkson Creek, with fine scenic views of the Camel Estuary and Padstow Bay.

PENHALE MINE

D.   1850-1853
L.   2 miles E of St. Issy SW962722
M/O. 62 tons copper
S.   Working on the opposite side of the valley to Legossick, Penhale's burrows, now partly obscured by undergrowth, can be located near the bottom of the valley to the west of Whitecross.

TRELOW

D.   1860-1872
L.   1 mile W of St. Jidgey SW922695
M/O. No records
S.   Although part of the area near Trelow Farm has recently become a centre for shire horses, signs of former mining activity can still be seen near the stream flowing north from Trelow Downs. The remains here consist of some scattered waste tips and a line of shaft burrows to the south of the farm, near a small wood.

PAWTON MINE

D.   1861-1883
L.   1¼ miles SE of St. Issey SW953702
M/O. 15,000 tons of iron ore
S.   The site of Pawton Mine, one of the larger setts in this area, is reached by taking the footpath from West Park Farm to Pawton Farm. The dumps and excavations of the mine now lie amongst woodland on the valley slopes between these two farms, and are easily accessible.

WHEAL TREWORNAN

D.   1822-1826
L.   1¼ miles N of Wadebridge SW979743
M/O. 20 tons copper
S.   The adit of this small copper mine can be located today on the low cliffline west of Trewornan Farm. The workings which were formerly situated in the fields above the adit have now been ploughed over. This site also affords splendid views over the River Camel and Padstow.

NORTH PORTHILLY

D.   1860-1868
L.   1¼ miles S of Polzeath SW933764
M/O. 28 tons lead
S.   The grassed-over burrows of the lead mine still survive near the middle of St. Enodoc golf course, near Rock. These now appear as grassy

hummocks amidst the dunes on the course, although the waste material in these mounds indicates former mining activity.

POLZEATH CONSOLS

D.   1847-1855

L.   Polzeath SW939791

M/O. A few tons of lead

S.   This group was an amalgamation of several small lead prospects working the valley sides between the village and Shilla Mill, amongst them Wheal Caroline, Wheal Phillipa and Tinner's Hill. Some dumps relating to this group can be located above the valley and in woods near the footbridge that crosses the stream at Shilla Mill.

Bodmin - St. Neot - Liskeard

TOLDISH (RUTHVOES)

D.   Group: 1855-1902, re-worked 1940's

L.   ½ mile NE of Indian Queens SW923600

M/O. 19,090 tons haematite; 1,380 tons iron; 1,022 tons maganese; quantities of ochre

Plate 13: *Toldish*

36

S.	An iron lode some ¾ mile in length, coursing across what is now the A30 road near Indian Queens, has been worked in the past by three mines, namely Treliver (on the northern part of the property), Ruthvoes and Toldish to the south. These were also in operation under the general name of Indian Queens Iron Mine. The only remains now left from this group can be found to the east of the road from the A30 to Ruthvoes, where a very prominent, well-preserved chimney stack stands in a field, together with some ore-treatment buildings which are also in good condition.

PARKA MINE

D.	1873-1883
L.	South of St. Columb Road SW911587
M/O.	580 tons tin
S.	This sett also worked with the adjoining Fatwork and Virtue Mine under the general name of Indian Queens Consols. Although the burrows are now covered in gorse and brambles,a chimney stack in good condition can be seen today on waste ground to the west of the A39 into St. Columb road village.

Plate 14: *Parka*

BRYNN MINE

D.	circa 1870's
L.	1¼ miles N of Roche SW991624
M/O.	18 tons tin
S.	This mine worked tin lodes both by opencast methods and by shafts. A large quarry, now fenced for safety and partly filled with vegetation, is situated in a field slightly west of Hill House.

MULBERRY

D.	1859-1916
L.	1½ miles NW of Lanivet SX019658
M/O.	1,300 tons tin
S.	Tin lodes to the north of Lanivet have been quarried in the past rather than worked by shafts, and Mulberry is the most impressive of these

Plate 15: *Mulberry Stockwork*

openworks left to be seen in this area, a sheer-sided chasm over 120 ft. deep carved out of the granite of Mulberry Downs. Falls of rock and dense vegetation now make it almost impossible to enter this awesome man-made excavation.

WHEAL PROSPER

D.   1846-1910, re-worked 1930 and 1951
L.   ½ mile W of Lanivet SX030642
M/O. Only 360 tons of tin recorded
S.   This is another equally impressive excavation beside the road to Lamorick, where an estimated 2 million tons of rock has been removed to form this vast pit. In recent years, this quarry has been used as a rubbish disposal tip for the Bodmin area.

WHEAL MARY LOUISE (TREBELL CONSOLS)

D.   1852-1866
L.   1¼ miles SE of Lanivet SX055633
M/O. 16 tons tin
S.   The chimney stack that used to stand on the site of this unproductive tin producer has now been demolished, although the foundation walls can still be located in thickets on the hilltop above Fentonpits, together with some gorse-covered burrows.

38

MAUDLIN MINE
D.   1823-1870
L.   3 miles E of Lanivet SX086625
M/O. 110 tons copper; 2 tons tin
S.   A few overgrown dumps and a shaft can be located on the valley side, near the stream flowing into the River Fowey.

RESTORMEL IRON MINE
D.   1855-1910
L.   ¾ mile N of Lostwithiel SX098613
M/O. 128,000 tons iron ore
S.   The ore at this particular site, the largest of Cornwall's iron mines, was excavated by quarries, and a pit of considerable dimensions can be seen a short distance north of Barngate Farm, although this is now on private property.

DUKE OF CORNWALL
D.   1855-1858
L.   2¼ miles N of Lostwithiel SX105629
M/O. 3,900 tons copper
S.   A few scattered dumps and a collapsed shaft or adit issuing a stream of ochrous water can be found in woods to the south of the road near Bofarnel.

PENBUGLE AND LANCARFE CONSOLS
D.   1842-1853
L.   1 mile N of Bodmin SX070689
M/O. No records - lead
S.   The mine lies in a quiet and secluded valley near Clerkenwater. Two adits and a shaft can still be located in the woods north of Penbugle Farm. One adit and the single shaft are on private property near the lodge in Pill Wood, adjacent to the stream. The other adit is beside the track that heads in a north easterly direction into Helland Wood.

TRESELLYN AND SCADDICK CONSOLS
D.   1851-1894
L.   1¼ miles N of Bolventor SX188787
M/O. 4 tons tin
S.   The scattered burrows of this small tin mine can be seen in the vicinity

of Trezeland and Towerhill, on Bodmin Moor. More old workings are further west on moorland above the River Fowey.

HALVANA MINE

D.   circa 1850's, re-opened 1915-1918
L.   1¾ miles S of Altarnun SX216786
M/O.   No records - tin and wolfram
S.   The workings of this mine are situated in Halvana Plantation, best reached by taking the track from Tregirls which leads into the woods. A few pits, walls and overgrown mounds are all that remain to be seen, although conifers now hide most of these old excavations from view.

EAST JANE

D.   1862-1864
L.   2¼ miles SE of Cardinham SX136656
M/O.   325 tons lead
S.   The remains of this small lead mine are situated in Cabilla Wood, on the north bank of the River Fowey. Some opencuts and walls can be located in a conifer plantation, beside one of the steep woodland tracks that traverse this area.

TREVEDDOE (CABILLA)

D.   1823-1909
L.   ½ mile NW of Warleggan SX152696
M/O.   Quantities of tin and copper
S.   Part of this mine was worked for tin in the massive man-made excavation known locally as Old Wheal Whisper, which itself dates back to the 15th. century. This awesome elongated pit, over 100 ft. deep at it's upper end, is now overgrown in part with trees and bushes and can be reached either through the woods to the east of the stream, or from one of the tracks near Treveddoe Farm. The latter route takes one to the topmost edge of this excavation, now heavily barb-wired for safety. To the east of Treveddoe, the same lodes were exploited on Warleggan Downs by a mine called GOOD - A - FORTUNE (SX157698). A shallow quarry hidden by ferns can still be located from this working on the Downs, near the footpath.

GOONZION

D.   1836-1864
L.   ½ mile W of St. Neot SX181677
M/O.   Small quantities of tin and copper

S.   A few mounds, walls and undulations, now mostly covered in ferns, can be seen to the south of the road from St. Neot, on Goonzion Downs. These downs were worked for tin and copper by shallow trenches as far back as the 17th. century, but very little remains from this long period of activity today in this area.

HOBB'S HILL MINE

D.   1844-1849
L.   1 mile N of St. Neot SX186693
M/O. 24 tons tin
S.   This mine was worked by both opencast quarrying and shafts. Two old excavations can be traced on the steep slopes of Hobb's Hill, above the St. Neot River. The site of this mine is reached by taking the lane to Trewindle, and then proceeding over the trackway that crosses the hill in an eastwards direction.

Plate 17: *Burrows of Wheal Robins*

WHEAL ROBINS

D.   1839-1856
L.   ¼ mile N of St. Neot SX183684
M/O. No records - copper and tin
S.   Although there are no records of any production from this mine, a shaft dump of considerable size can be seen in a field to the west of Hilltown. Also on the site are the ruined remains of an old miner's cottage.

41

NEW SOUTH CARADON

D. 1856-1865
L. ½ mile W of Commonmoor SX230692
M/O. No recorded output - copper
S. Virtually an unproductive trial for copper lodes believed to emanate from South Caradon, this mine worked on the steep slopes of Bulland Downs, where two large shaft dumps can be seen today, near South Trekeive Farm.

Plate 16: *Wheal Victoria*

WHEAL VICTORIA

D. 1844-1855
L. 1 mile SW of Commonmoor, in Draynes Wood SX223687
M/O. No records - copper
S. Although this small and long forgotten prospect was abandoned so long ago, the well-preserved granite walls of the mine's water wheel pit still stand near Golitha Falls in the peaceful and picturesque surroundings of Draynes Wood. The gated-up mouth of the adit can also be located in a low bank nearer to Draynes Bridge.

WHEAL NORRIS
D.   1852-1880
L.   ¾ mile NE of Commonmoor SX248698
M/O.   104 tons tin; some copper
S.   A few gorse covered waste tips and broken walls are all that remain from this unproductive prospect, in a field to the east of Goatlands Farm.

CARADON COPPER MINE
D.   1844-1851
L.   ½ mile SE of Crow's Nest SX272689
M/O.   No records - copper
S.   One of the numerous but less well known setts that mushroomed during the fabulous success of nearby South Caradon, this site can be identified today by a large overgrown burrow in a field to the south of Higher Trethake.

EAST CARADON
D.   1860-1885
L.   1 mile S of Upton Cross SX276704
M/O.   54,000 tons copper
S.   East Caradon exploited the eastern extensions of the South Caradon lodes, and is identifiable today by an enormous burrow on the slope of Caradon Hill, above the track of the long dis-used railway.

SHARPTOR
D.   1865-1872
L.   1 mile W of Darleyford SX260731
M/O.   Small quantities of tin and copper
S.   The considerable dumps, shafts and the base walls of a stack still survive on this mostly unproductive sett which is situated at over 900 ft. above sea level. Fine panoramic views can be had over North East Cornwall from this site.

DARLEY MINE
D.   1850-1887
L.   North west of Darleyford SX273733
M/O.   7 tons copper
S.   The dumps of this unsuccessful copper producer can be seen on high

ground to the north of the Darleyford to Henwood road, near Notter Tor.

WESTCOTT MINE
D.   1842-1846
L.   1¼ miles NE of Upton Cross SX292738
M/O. No records - lead
S.   This old, unproductive lead producer is situated in the steep wooded slopes of Colquite Wood above the River Lynher. To the north of the road, near the bridge, is a large quarry-like excavation with other old overgrown pits in the surrounding woods. The mine's leat commences at the foot of this quarry and can be traced in woods to the south of the road, eventually terminating on the banks of the Lynher

BERRIOW
D.   1844-1875
L.   ½ mile S of North Hill SX271757
M/O. No records - zinc and copper
S.   The few remains left from this mine can be located between West Berriow Farm and the road bridge, where some slatey burrows survive in fields on the edge of Rocky Wood.

TREBARTHA LEMARNE
D.   1880-1887
L.   1¼ miles NW of North Hill SX256777
M/O. 20 tons tin; 18 tons mispickel; 20 tons arsenic
S.   The overgrown dumps of this mine now lie on private property in a wood adjoining the Lemarne Plantation. The mine was re-opened in 1951 for wolfram, with limited results.

Callington - Gunnislake

WHEAL GILL
D.   1840-1862, re-worked 1901
L.   1½ miles NW of St. Ive Cross SX295677
M/O. Quantities of copper, lead and zinc
S.   Some dumps and a single shaft remain from this lead mine, in woods to the north of Hay Wood, above the River Tiddy. This mine was last

worked at the beginning of this century under the name of Hayford United.

BENEATHWOOD MINE
D. 1858-1889
L. South of Plushabridge SX305723
M/O. 5 tons lead
S. Some grassed-over burrows can be seen in fields between Beneathwood Farm and the River Lynher. Another dump which could possibly be associated with this mine is in a field adjacent to Lower Addicroft Farm (SX302726).

CARADON WOOD MINE
D. 1851-1854
L. ½ mile S of Plushabridge SX305716
M/O. No records - lead
S. The sett of this old, unproductive lead mine is situated in dense undergrowth near the southern bank of the River Lynher, and consists of an over grown wheel pit and some dumps. This mine is very difficult to reach - there are few tracks in these woods whose sides drop almost vertically to the river bank.

WHEAL IDA
D. 1863-1872
L. 1½ miles N of St. Ive Cross SX303692
M/O. No records - lead
S. This small, insignificant venture, which was little more than a trial for lead, is still identifiable today by a surviving slatey burrow in a field to the south of Fillamore Farm.

TOR WOOD
D. circa 1870's
L. ¾ mile NW of Pillaton SX356650
M/O. No recorded output - manganese
S. An interesting and long forgotten prospect that worked for manganese in the sheer-sided slopes of Tor Wood, in the Lynher Valley. When the mine was in operation, three levels were being utilised. A caved-in depression beside the road near the weir probably indicates the position of the lower level. There appears to be no trace now left of the upper level, which has no doubt collapsed and is now hidden by undergrowth. However, the middle level was still open and accessible in 1987,

although this is very difficult to locate because of the absence of trackways in Tor Wood which is, as previously mentioned, almost vertical in places.

WHEAL LEIGH

D.   circa 1860's
L.   1¼ miles N of Landrake SX381626
M/O. No recorded output - antimony
S.   The most conspicuous feature remaining from this mine, which was believed to have been in operation in the 16th. century, is a burrow of considerable size in the middle of a field to the south of Leigh Farm, and east of the road. The wheel pit and dressing floors are now mostly obscured by undergrowth a short distance east of this burrow, on the banks of the stream, together with the caved-in mouth of the adit.

WHEAL SHEBA (WEST WHEAL MARTHA)

D.   1854-1864
L.   ¾ mile W of Luckett SX376736
M/O. 5,862 tons copper
S.   The dumps and shafts of this mine, also in operation under the names of Trehill and Kellyhole, now lie in sparse woodland on the steep bank of the stream, south of the lane from Broadgate to Oldmill.

STOKE CLIMSLAND CONSOLS

D.   1851-1858
L.   1½ miles N of Luckett SX388762
M/O. No records - lead and copper
S.   A small, isolated lead prospect working in the steep wooded area between Underhill Farm and Trecombe to the north west. The only sign of any former mining activity in this secluded area today is a long slaty burrow in a field slightly north of the building on Underhill Farm, and to the west of the lane leading into the woods.

WEST DRAKEWALLS

D.   circa 1870's
L.   1¼ miles W of Gunnislake SX409707
M/O. No records - copper
S.   Although both Prince of Wales Mine and Drakewalls border on this sett to the east and west, production was somewhat less successful at this site. Some grassed-over dumps in fields to the west of the Honicombe camping site can still be seen today.

North West Cornwall, North Cornwall and Launceston

GILSONS COVE

D.   circa 1830's
L.   ¼ mile SW of Portquin SW966803
M/O. No records - lead
S.   Two shafts and some scattered tips can be seen on the cliffs near Portquin, probably the result of trials for lead and copper along this stretch of coastline - more scanty signs of mining are evident on Reedy Cliff about ¾ mile to the north east (SW975809)

TREWETHEN

D.   Earlier dates unknown. Re-worked in the 1940's
L.   2 miles N of St. Tudy SX501790
M/O. No records - lead, zinc and antimony
S.   Some old gorse-covered mounds can still be seen in fields to the east of Trewethen Farm. These probably date from the mine's earlier and unrecorded dates of operation.

PENGENNA

D.   circa 1860's
L.   1¾ miles N of St. Tudy SX051786
M/O. 16 tons antimony
S.   The adit of this mine is situated in woods near the stream flowing south of Pengenna Farm. Near the portal is an overgrown dump, difficult to locate because of the dense vegetation in the small valley where this mine now lies.

EAST GILBERT AND MERRYMEETING

D.   circa 1830-1840
L.   2¼ miles SE of St. Tudy SX089733
M/O. No records - tin and copper
S.   A rather remote and little known copper prospect whose site can still be found today by locating a small, overgrown burrow in the corner of a field directly north of the building at Merrymeeting Farm, to the east of the River Camel.

TREORE

D.   Earlier dates unknown. Re-worked 1915-1918

L.   1½ miles E of Port Isaac SX020801

M/O.   No records - some quantities of antimony, lead, gold and silver

S.   The workings of this mine, which exploited an interesting but unproductive lead lode, lie on the north bank of the stream flowing into Port Isaac, below Treore Farm. Only some gorse-covered tips can be seen today.

WHEAL BEENY

D.   Circa 1840's

L.   1¼ miles NE of Boscastle SX109927

M/O.   No records - lead and silver

S.   Unproductive trials for lead, copper and silver were carried out on Beeny Cliff in the 1840's, but few records exist regarding dates and output. The only sign left today of any former mining activity on the cliffs here is a slatey burrow near the 300 ft. contour line, adjacent to the cliff path.

ST. GENNY'S MINE

D.   circa 1830's, prospected 1914 and 1936

L.   1¼ miles E of Crackington Haven SX159961

M/O.   No records - zinc

S.   An unfamiliar and rather isolated mine working for zinc in a steeply wooded and secluded valley to the north of Crackington hamlet. Two filled-in shafts in the grounds of the cottages named 'Mineshop' can be located today, together with the portal of the adit which is adjacent to the stream near the cottages.

TREDARRUP

D.   circa 1850's

L.   2½ miles SE of Marshgate SX191903

M/O.   No records - iron and maganese

S.   A large, overgrown burrow still survives from this unproductive mine, near the building at Tredarrup Farm. Some depressions in the fields to the north of the farm indicate the shafts which have now been filled-in.

TREGUNE

D. 1846-1865
L. 1¼ miles SE of Altarnun SX231792
M/O. 56 tons copper
S. This mine is situated west of the sett of Treburland Mine, and the site is marked today by a few scattered waste tips to the east of Tregune Farm.

TREBURLAND MINE

D. 1881-1890, re-worked 1914 and 1940
L. 1½ miles SE of Altarnun SX237794
M/O. Quantities of tin and wolfram
S. The relatively shallow workings of this mine now lie in thickets and swampy undergrowth to the south of the ford near Trevague. The ruined wall of an old building, possibly a dry, stand in the woods adjacent to the footpath and the stream.

TREVELL

D. 1850-1852
L. 1 mile S of Polyphant SX253812
M/O. No records - lead
S. A classic example of an old men's working in a remote setting, Trevell Mine is situated in steep woods on the south side of the stream known as Penpont Water, and immediately west of Trevell Farm. An old track near the farm leads into these woods. In 1987, the mine's large wheel-pit and leat could still be traced with difficulty, a large amount of vegetation having taken over the site. The mouth of the adit is visible in the stream bank, but the single shaft is now hidden by trees and undergrowth on the steep wooded slopes.

TREBURTLE (TREWETLE)

D. circa 1860's
L. 2 miles NW of Egloskerry SX255891
M/O. No records - unproductive trials for copper
S. An overgrown dump can be located with difficulty in swampy undergrowth near the ford at the end of Treburtle Wood. A few scattered burrows can also be seen in the vicinity of Lower Penrose Farm, a short distance north of the River Ottery.

Plate 18: *Burrow at Treglum Mill*

WHEAL EMMA AND WHEAL JOB

D.   1860-1890

L.   1 mile NW of Badgall SX222873

M/O. No records - trials for silver and lead on Treglum Downs

S.   Two large burrows exist on the Downs from these old prospects - one is near Trew Farm, the other on high ground to the south of Treglum Cottage at SX227872. There is also an unidentifiable burrow in a field on the north bank of the stream near Treglum Mill at SX232869 which could be associated with these trials.

LIDCOTT

D.   1875-1881

L.   1 mile SE of Badgall SX241850

M/O. 310 tons manganese

S.   Lidcott Mine exploited a manganese deposit on Laneast Downs, and the shallow workings today lie in dense undergrowth a short distance south east of Lidcott hamlet.

LAWHITTON CONSOLS

D.   1860-1865

L.   2¼ miles SE of Launceston SX364831

M/O. No records - lead and copper

S.   The site of this mine, which was little more than a trial, is still identifiable today by a long slatey burrow on the south bank of the stream that flows into the Tamar, a short distance north east of Lawhitton Barton. There are now no traces of the mine's adit which could formerly be seen opposite this burrow on the stream's north bank.